CW00410115

Piano
Grade 2

Pieces & Exercises
for Trinity College London exams

2015-2017

Published by
Trinity College London
www.trinitycollege.com

Registered in England
Company no. 02683033
Charity no. 1014792

Printed in England by Caligraving Ltd.

Gavotte

William Boyce
(1711-1779)

Ländler

Franz Schubert
(1797-1828)

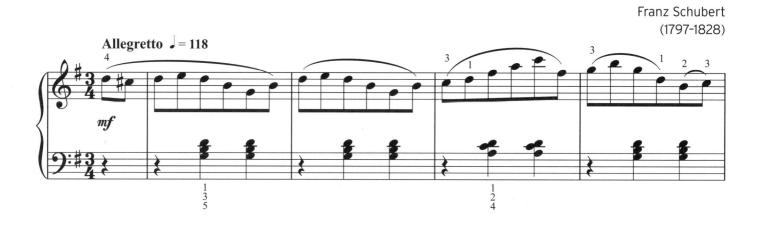

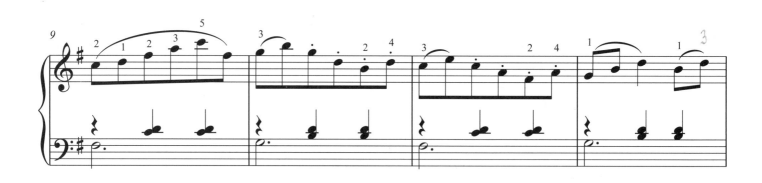

4

Allegro un peu louré

from *Giselle*

Arr. Janet and Alan Bullard

Adolphe Adam
(1803–1856)

Willow, tit-willow

from *The Mikado*

Arr. Janet and Alan Bullard

Arthur Sullivan
(1842–1900)

Mexican March

David Cullen
(born 1942)

Street Beat

Alan Bullard
(born 1947)

FreuDich / Feelicitous

Michael Proksch
(born 1958)

l.h. staccato

All dynamics are editorial

The Penguin Parade

Christine Donkin
(born 1967)

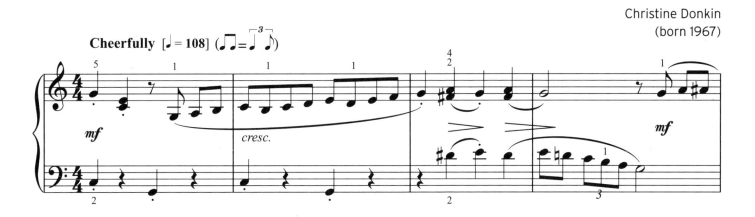

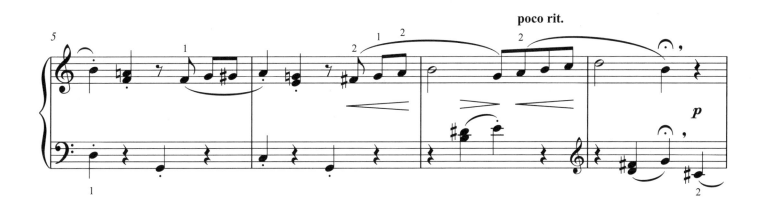

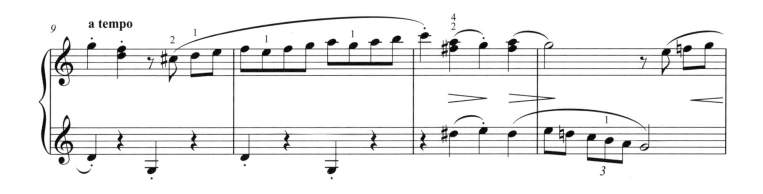

Composer's original metronome mark is ♩ = 126

The Swing Detectives

Ben Crosland
(born 1968)

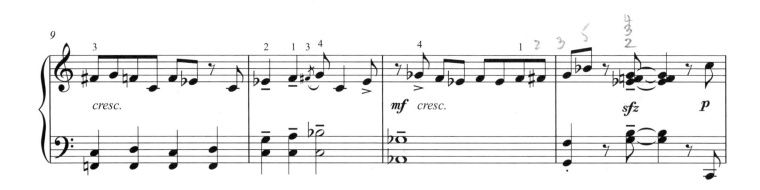

Exercises

1a. Revolving Door – tone, balance and voicing

1b. No Reply – tone, balance and voicing

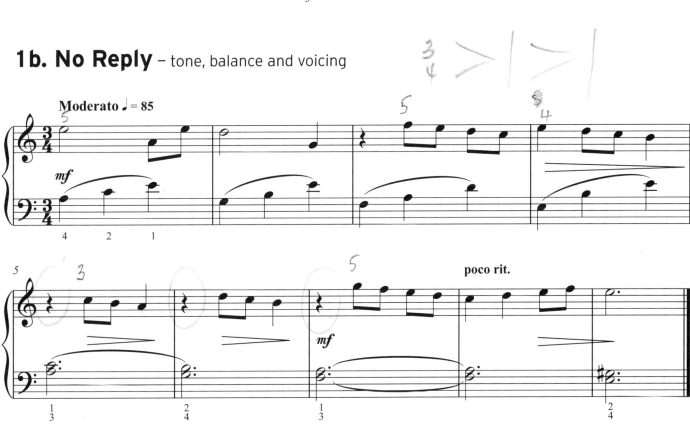

2a. Hot Coals – co-ordination

2b. Pins and Needles – co-ordination

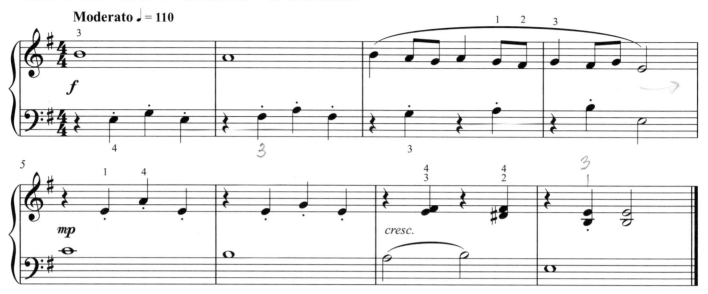

3a. Chill Factor – finger & wrist strength and flexibility

3b. Creepy Goings-on – finger & wrist strength and flexibility